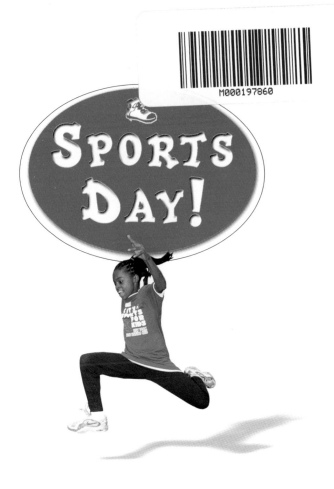

by Julian Ramirez

Harcourt

Orlando   Boston   Dallas   Chicago   San Diego

Visit *The Learning Site!*

www.harcourtschool.com

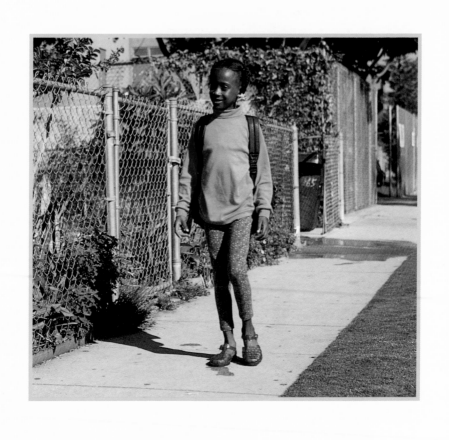

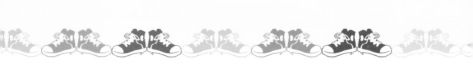

Angela can walk.

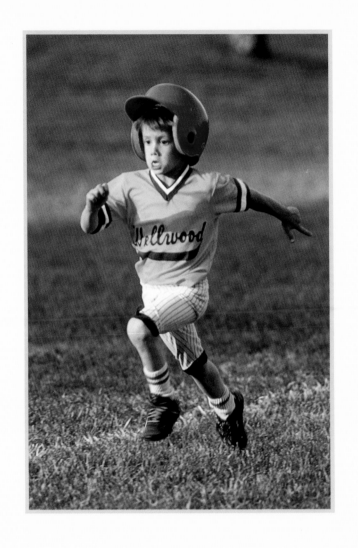

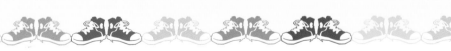

Ben can run.

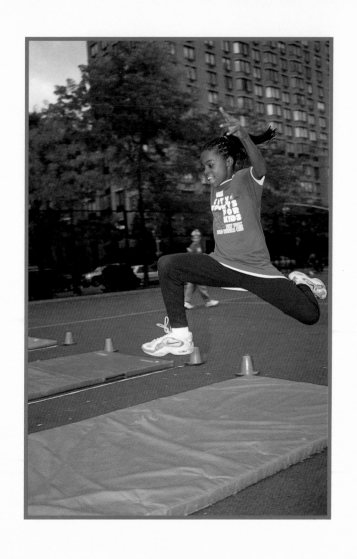

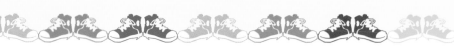

Nina can jump.

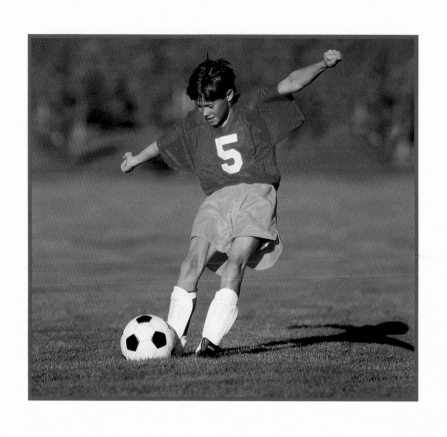

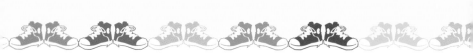

Ramón can kick.

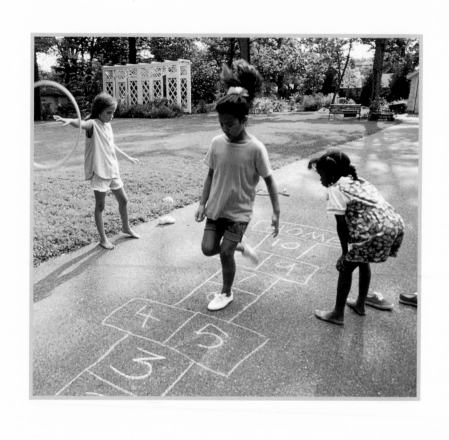

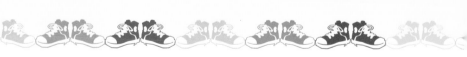

Jess can hop.

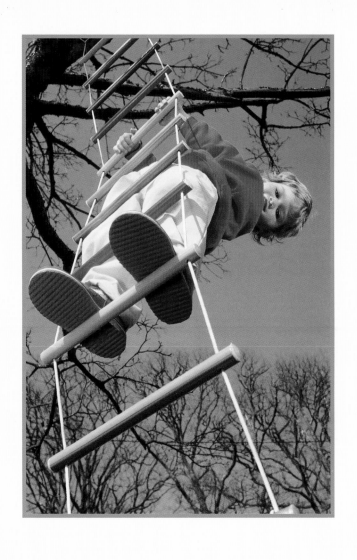

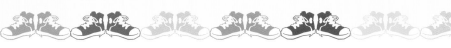

Mark can climb.

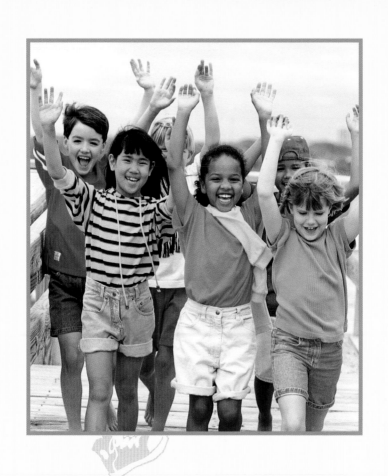

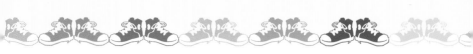

It's Sports Day!